F

G

COVER
A school of Striped Porkfish swims by

FRONT ENDPAPERS:
- *A · Spanish Hogfish*
- *B · Red Hind*
- *C · Grunts*
- *D · Gorgonian and Blueheads*
- *E · Young Blue Tang*
- *F · Sponges and Corals*
- *G · Diver and Mutton Snapper*
- *H · Staghorn Coral*
- *I · Shark*
- *J · Red Hind*

ACKNOWLEDGMENTS: *Author and publisher gratefully acknowledge the cooperation of Marineland of Florida, the world's first oceanarium, in making available scenes from the theatrical feature film "Secrets of the Reef", produced by the author. These pictures, © copyright 1956 by Marineland of Florida, appear on pages 2, 27, 28, 29, 31, 32, 33, 37, 42, 46 and 47. All other photographs in the book © copyright 1964 by Jerry Greenberg, including those by Ed Fisher which appear on pages 2, 16, 23, 25, 37, 39, 47.*

PUBLISHED BY
PAUL HAMLYN LIMITED • Westbook House • Fulham Broadway • London

THE CORAL REEF

BY ALFRED BUTTERFIELD

PHOTOGRAPHS BY

JERRY GREENBERG

AND ED FISHER

PAUL HAMLYN · LONDON

Look down through the warm, clear waters of the coral reef, or better still slip quietly into them, and you enter a world of beauty and wonder that is like no other of sea or land. Towers, terraces, colonnades, archways, galleries, domes, and spires of coral surround you. Branching antlers of staghorn coral reach up towards the sunlit surface. Convoluted boulders of brain coral loom below. ■ Red, green, and yellow encrusting corals splash the rocks; graceful sea fans and sea rods, in crimson, purple, and gold, sway in the surge of the ocean currents. Here many-hued sponges grow; tubeworms extend their painted heads from limestone burrows; and delicate sea anemones beckon with their rose and lavender tentacles.

■ In the coral reef, where food and shelter are plentiful, living things of all colours, shapes, patterns, forms, and sizes flourish—from the scarcely visible, drifting creatures of the plankton, on which the food-cycle of the reef depends, to huge reef-visitors like the shark and giant manta ray—from the swift, smart, sensitive octopus, to its humble cousin the mollusc. ■ The architects of this busy, beautiful community in the sea are the reef-building corals—small animals that construct their cup-shaped limestone homes on top of those of departed ancestors. They are members of the same class of animals (Anthozoa) as the sea fans and sea anemones. Nearly all the spectacular sights of the reef are animals (or monuments constructed

7

by animals such as the coral polyps) rather than plants. Thousands of years ago, here where the water is shallow, sunny, and warm and the currents fresh and strong and teeming with microscopic food, a few coral polyps settled down. They found footholds on an offshore rock or boulder, the sloping sides of an extinct undersea volcano, or some other firm anchorage on the ocean bottom. They grew and budded and multiplied, each small coral polyp extracting carbonate of lime from the sea and adding its own limestone skeleton to those of its predecessors. ■ This is the way the reef is built: by infinite numbers of creatures building towards the sun, year after year, century after century. Tubeworms build calcareous burrows in, under, and around the coral formations, cementing them together. ■ Stony algae, an ancient marine plant, weaves its limy skeleton among them to bind the structure still more firmly. As time goes on,

physical and chemical action consolidates these elements (and others such as coral sands and empty shells) into solid coralline limestone. ■ All this limestone is extracted from the sea itself, of course, so in a sense it is the sea that builds the coral reef—the sea and the sun. For where the light and warmth of the sun cannot penetrate strongly (100 to 150 feet), the coral polyps cannot grow. ■ One reason for this is that within the body of each polyp are microscopic plants that make a vital contribution to its digestive process. Like all plants, they are totally dependent on photosynthesis. Without sunlight, they die. Then the polyps die too. ■ All the world's coral reefs are in moderately shallow water. Some, however, are hundreds of feet thick—the result of the fact that the ocean floor has sunk (or the water level risen) at approximately the same rate as the corals have been building their way up towards the surface.

9

Gorgonians

Soft corals and horny corals like the sea fans and sea rods lend beauty and colour to the reef landscape, but the great reef builders are stony Madrepore corals, such as staghorn, brain, and Porite. ■ Long-lasting as their monuments are, the reef-building creatures are very fragile in life. The temperature of the water must not fall below 68 to 70 degrees Fahrenheit, its salinity and overall chemical balance must be just right, and the current must be strong and clean—constantly replenishing the corals' food supply and carrying away waste and impurities. Many corals thrive best on the seaward side of the reef. If exposed to air, they perish. ■ Coral formations grow at widely varying rates, depending on type, age and local conditions. Most Pacific corals grow faster than Atlantic. Reefs grow at a rate of from 5 to 200 centimeters per year, and may have developed in from

10,000 to 30,000 years. ■ Brain coral (Meandra) rises in great, round boulders on the floor of the reef and along its sides. Labyrinthine convolutions, like those of the human brain, cover all its exposed surface. Each of the numerous walled compartments in the labyrinth houses a single coral polyp. These massive, stony corals are bulwarks of the reef. ■ Stinging corals be-

Brain Coral; Close-up of Brain Coral

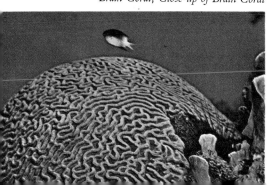

long to a different class (Hydrozoa) from the true corals (Anthozoa) and are important reef-builders. These Millepore corals are the stronghold of thousands of minute polyps that protrude their heads through pinprick pores in the limestone to gather in their microscopic food. ■ The polyps' tiny tentacles are equipped with powerful stinging cells, or nematocysts. Brushed against by the unwary reef creature or human they can inflict a painful injury. ■ The buoyancy of sea water enables coral formations like these to assume towering, top-heavy shapes that would be impossible on land, where gravity would topple them. Strong as they are, however, they are vulnerable to ocean storms. Huge chunks of coral may be tossed up on shore by the raging waves, where they become buried in the sand, or are ground up into sand themselves. ■ When the water is quiet, these towers and ramparts of stinging coral are among the love-liest sights in the reef. They are a favourite haunt of small, gaily marked fishes, some of whom merely rely on these stinging walls for protection from larger creatures, and some of whom nibble away the coral themselves. ■ The rainbow parrotfish breaks off the hard coral cups with its sharp, strong beak, pulverizes them with special grinders in its throat, then swallows the living polyps within. (Coral polyps themselves feed at night, hiding within their homes by day.) ■ Other predators seem to relish even such apparently unappetizing creatures as the sea anemone, whose defences are like those of its cousin, the stinging coral. Some shell-less snails, in fact, not only eat sea anemones, but store up the anemones' stinging cells in their own bodies—using them later for their *own* defence! ■ There are other creatures,

Rock Beauty Swims Over Fortress of Stinging Corals

such as the placid sponge, who accept the hospitality of the coral reef without attacking their hosts. ∎ Sponges, which have a whole phylum (Porifera) to themselves, vary widely in colour, size and structure. Some have a hard, stiff skeleton; others (like the bath sponge) a flexible one; still others no skeleton at all. They are seldom eaten by other reef-dwellers, and they them-

Red Sponges and Sea Fan　　　　*Tube Sponge*

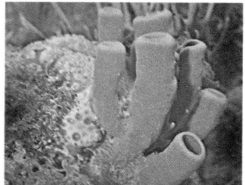

selves play host to many small crustaceans, worms, and molluscs. ■ After a free-swimming larval stage, lasting only a few hours, sponges settle down in the reef and stay in one spot. Their principal activity is pumping water through their bodies by means of countless little flagella. A sponge only 4 inches high filters 25 gallons of water a day.

Sponge and Coral

Tubeworms ▶

Banded Butterfly Fish

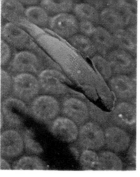

Royal Gramma

Sharpnose Puffer

Adult Bluehead

16

The corals are the masterbuilders, but the lords of the reef are the fishes. They are its dominant form of life: the most highly developed, the most aggressive and—even in these surroundings—the most colourful. Many reef species, like the exotic royal gramma, are 2-3 inches long. Others, like the yellow grunt, grow to a foot or two. While the giant grouper may reach 6-8 feet, and a weight of six hundredweight, most reef-dwelling fishes are of modest dimensions compared to their open-sea cousins. ■ Characteristically, reef fishes are more compact, with broader tails and stubbier fins for making short turns and quick starts and stops in the jagged coral. Here, alertness and mobility are at least as important as size. But by far the most striking thing about the reef fishes is the splendid variety of their shapes, markings, and colours.

Bluestriped Grunts in Coral Opening

The reds, blues, yellows, greens of the reef-dwelling fishes—all the primary colours and every subtle shading in between—dazzle the observer's eye. The queen angelfish, trailing gossamer wings above and below its chrome-yellow tailfin, is clothed in a tapestry of light blue, dark blue, gold, and scarlet. Its cousin, the French angelfish, is black with vivid yellow stripes. The four-eyed butterfly fish is a china-white disc within a yellow border, and wears a "false eye" near its tail. Two-inch-long neon gobies are streaks of electric blue, framed in gleaming black. ■ There are multi-coloured sea fans, sponges, tunicates, sea anemones, tubeworms and corals; pink, beige, yellow, and spotted snails; the scarlet-fringed lima shell; the scallop with its bright ring of eyes; red and blue crabs.

*Queen Angelfish
and French Grunt*

*Smooth Trunkfish
in Coral Grotto*

The function of all these riotous hues, these madcap markings, is by no means fully understood. No doubt the coral reef was colourful long before the fishes, for example, arrived here. Those creatures whose colours and patterns fitted in best with their surroundings perhaps enjoyed an advantage in survival. However, habits and needs, mobility and responsiveness, mechanisms of attack and defence, vary tremendously among reef-dwellers; and yet nearly all of them display colours and patterns of a boldness and brilliance encountered nowhere else in the sea. ■ Thinking of camouflage on land, where creatures are often the same colour as their background, we might conclude that the gaily marked reef-dwellers are benefitting similarly, and perhaps some of them are. ■ But colours and markings may have a number of

Yellowtail Damselfish and Stinging Coral

different functions, among them concealment or confusion (which we generally think of as camouflage), warning, recognition, aids to courtship (roughly translatable as sex appeal). It is difficult to evaluate all these considerations among reef fishes. The young of many species are much less vividly coloured than their parents. Perhaps this gives them maximum protection when they need it most. Certainly nothing could be more conspicuous than a yellow-and-blue adult yellow grunt swimming in front of a lavender sea fan. ■ One theory about the exotic colours of reef-dwellers suggests that these characteristics have been perpetuated simply because they didn't turn out to be insuperable disadvantages in this setting, though in a less colourful one they might have meant the end of the line.

Yellow Grunt and Sea Fans

A

B

C

D

E

F

22

G

H

I

Large or small, bold or shy, garish or subtle in their colours and patterns, the fishes of the reef are more than a match for the beauty of their surroundings. For the most part, they are species that are found nowhere else in the sea

A · School of Striped Grunts
B · Young Blue Tang
C · Butter Hamlet
D · Marbled Groupers
E · Sergeant Major
F · Four-Eyed Butterfly Fish
G · Queen Angelfish
H · Snook
I · Young French Angelfish

When we view even a random sampling of reef fishes we are staggered by the innumerable approaches that have been made, through long eons of evolution, to the problems and opportunities of life. The relatively uncommon rock beauty is famous for its speed and maneuverability and for the way it uses the protection of the reef. The rock beauty's striking costume, which perhaps otherwise might be a hazard, is compensated for by its cautious habits. The shy cubbyu, like many of its croaker relatives, hides beneath the ledges of the reef. ■ The Nassau grouper, on the other hand, is a far-ranging hunter, prowling continually through the caverns and grottoes of the reef in search of moving prey. A member of the very large family of sea basses, it is striped and mottled in a multitude of colours, and blends into its background.

Rock Beauty Clings Close to Coral

1

2

3

4

5

6

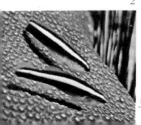

The yellowhead wrasse (1) a member of the wrasse family, goes through pronounced colour changes in growing up. "Kissing" chromis (2) may possibly be just removing parasites. Neon gobies (3) are two-inch streaks of luminescent beauty, hard to follow in the water, while the 2–3 ft. Nassau grouper (4) can run through several colour changes, from cream to dark reddish brown, in only a minute. The polka-dotted marine jewel (5) a member of the damselfish or demoiselle family, which is very prominent in the reef, is tiny but aggressive. The cubbyu (6) despite its bold stripes and conspicuous dorsal fin, is very shy

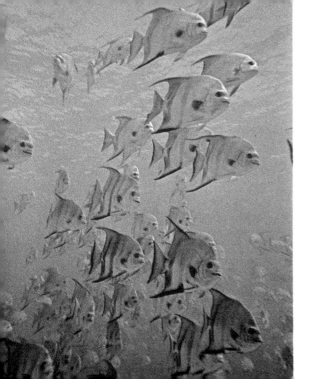

Over here a school of spadefish swims swiftly above the coral rocks. Over there a school of a thousand silver pilchards wheels in unison, catching the sun, then melting into the distance. Leaping through a pass in the coral comes a platoon of blue-and-yellow grunts. Near the bottom, a solitary bluehead bends solemnly through a grove of branching corals in its festive costume of bright blue, light blue, black, and forest green. ■ Feasting on the abundance of the reef, protected by its walls against the marauders of the open sea and all but the worst of storms, the fishes have prospered here through thousands of generations, developing special characteristics and habits in this special environment, and multiplying to fill every level of the reef with their beauty. They are this world's first citizens. But look closer and you see that the reef is the home of myriad other races—the invertebrates.

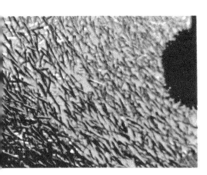

AT FAR LEFT, *a school of Atlantic spade-fish swims to safety. By keeping together in schools, fishes present a confusing target to their enemies. (Young fish are often less conspicuous than adults and blend into the distance more readily.)* ABOVE, *Pilchards, small herring-like fish, find security in numbers.* AT RIGHT, *bluestriped grunts, so named because they grunt, romp among coral banks*

Fishes, like mammals, birds, amphibians, and reptiles, belong to the only subkingdom or phylum of animal life (Chordata) that is gifted with a backbone. The Chordates, or vertebrates, number about 45,000 species. All other animals, numbering perhaps 1,000,000 species and hundreds of thousands of times more living individuals, are *invertebrates*. Some have an external skeleton or shell, others no skeleton at all. ■ The invertebrates as a whole are often spoken of as "lower" or more "primitive" than the vertebrates, to indicate that they came along earlier on the evolutionary time-scale. Yet they do quite as well as backboned animals in meeting the challenges that come their way, and in passing on the secrets of survival to their offspring. What's more, invertebrates are endlessly fascinating in the range and ingenuity of their special adaptations for living—nowhere more so than here in the coral reef.

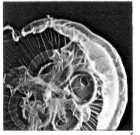

3

1. Florida Stone Crab
2. Pipefish
3. Moonjelly (*Aurelia*)
4. Common Octopus
5. Bristleworm
6. Banded Coral Shrimp
7. Arrow Crab
8. Tunicate "Tadpoles"
9. Flatworm
10. Eye of Pink Conch

The range of reef-dwelling invertebrates is immense; it includes the hard-shelled *molluscs* (such as oysters, scallops and snails and their cousins the octopuses and squids); the spiny-skinned *echinoderms* (sea urchins, starfishes, crinoids); the hollow-gutted *coelenterates* (corals, sea anemones, jellyfishes); the *porifera* (sponges); the many nations of *marine worms* (round, flat, and segmented and representing wholly different epochs in the history of life); and the very large phylum of the *arthropods* (creatures with jointed legs), which includes the innumerable crabs, shrimps, lobsters, crayfishes, and barnacles of the sea—and their cousins on land, the insects. ■ Many of these animals look like plants: the pink-tipped sea anemones; the tulip-shaped hydroids; the crinoid sea lilies; the sponges, tunicates, sea fans, sea rods and encrusting corals of the reef's "gardens". Some spend their lives rooted to one spot; others swim freely. Still others are mobile at one stage of life, sessile at another. ■ When one observes, in their own environment, the talents and aptitudes of such ancient creatures as the sponges, tubeworms, snails, jellyfishes and corals, one comes to feel that these efficient creatures are not "lowly" at all.

1

A plumeworm's many-hued head (1) splashes colour against its brain-coral background. A font-shaped sponge (2) lies nestled among corals. Floating by near the surface are the porpita (3), a colonial jellyfish only an inch across, and its larger cousins, the spectacular lion's mane jellyfish (5), and the beautiful spotted (or common) jellyfish (6). Down below, a tiny snail (4) climbs a sea fan

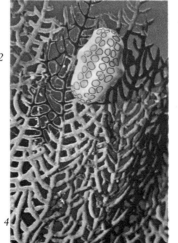

The eternal miracle of birth takes myriad forms in the reef. Many creatures release clouds of eggs into the sea, but only a few will reach maturity. Others provide the unborn young with strong, protecting egg-cases; or hide the eggs out of sight; or carry them constantly with them; or dig nests and stand guard over them. (The better the young are sheltered and cared for, the fewer are needed to carry on the race.) ■ A little shell-less snail, the sea pigeon, lays a spiral pattern of eggs among the protecting rocks of her own neighbourhood. The mother sea turtle, however, must make a long and difficult pilgrimage to bury her eggs high up on the beach. ■ The octopus, that remarkable, eight-armed mollusc whose unique talents range from rapid-change camouflage to jet-propulsion, is among the best of mothers. Fastening her eggs to the walls of her grotto, the mother octopus brushes them gently with her

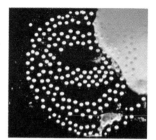

Sea-Pigeon Eggs

Pregnant Male Sea Horse

Tulip-Shell Eggs

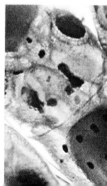

Baby Octopus in Egg

32

Father Sea Horse "Gives Birth"

arms and fans them with her breathing-siphon. As each octopus develops, its eyes, its pulsing heart and even its colour-cells become visible within the transparent shell. Finally the babies escape from the egg and the mother blows them out into open water. Most will quickly perish, but that is the way of the sea. ■ Among sea horses, on the other hand, it is the father who takes responsibility for the young. The mother simply deposits her eggs in the father's brood pouch, then swims away. Within six weeks the young sea horses are ready to emerge. Straining violently, and changing colour with each convulsive movement, the father sea horse expels his hundred-odd young—four, five, a dozen at a time. From the moment of birth the babies swim freely. Father settles down to rest. His own children may use him for a hitching post.

Spanish Hogfish

Everywhere in the reef, creatures are constantly
on the alert. Each happening is seen by thousands of eyes, sensed by thousands of sets of
receptors. The blue crab scuttling sideways
along the bottom is watched by the hungry
octopus from its cave; is felt (as much as seen)
by the buff-and-blue scrawled filefish and is
detected also by a cluster of beautiful tubeworms, who snap their flowerlike heads inside

French Grunts

their burrows at its approach. ■ Except for the timid tubeworms, none of the other reef-residents reacts visibly at the moment. But if the crab should come upon an appetizing coral shrimp—or if the crab itself should be attacked by the filefish or the octopus—the whole neighbourhood might erupt with action, the excitement communicating itself throughout the reef. The Spanish hogfish could be counted on to join in, and so could the spotted hind, another of the family of groupers. ■ Meanwhile the scene is tranquil. Reacting instantly to opportunity or danger, the creatures of the reef anticipate neither. Each species has its own ways of coping with life's problems, with hunting and being hunted, and with carrying on its own kind.

Scrawled Filefish

Longspine Squirrelfish

Glassy Sweeper

Any weakness or injury is an invitation to the hunter. Death—like birth—wears a thousand faces in the reef. ■ Marauders like the bull shark roam lazily along the edges of the reef looking for food. Sharks like the bull will attack anything when hungry or aroused. Growing to 7 feet and more, they are too big for the more crowded confines of the reef. ■ Deep in the caves and crannies of the reef lurk the 6-foot green moray eel and its 3-foot first cousin, the spotted moray. Without pectoral fins or well-defined tails, the fierce, sharp-toothed morays are fishes of an early type. ■ The 6-foot great barracuda is built for speed and striking power. A highly selective feeder, its rare attacks on humans are believed to be "mistakes" on its part. In general, the predators of the reef kill only what they are going to eat— there is neither waste nor deliberate cruelty in their killing.

AT FAR LEFT, *bull sharks laze along edge of reef. Remoras, or sharksuckers, go along for the ride. When sharks feed, remoras detach themselves and gobble up stray morsels, then come aboard again. AT RIGHT, the green moray eel protrudes its head from its cranny in the coral. BELOW, the 6-ft. lean great barracuda*

Against the ever-present hazards of life in the reef, Nature supplies a fascinating array of defences. The coral city itself is one of these. Its branching arms and protecting caverns shelter its inhabitants from the hunting hordes of the open sea. ■ Each species has its own defence: the spiny lobster's bristling external skeleton; the forbidding armour of the porcupine fish; the pink conch's fortress of stone; the green turtle's thick shell; the spotted, tufted, weedlike appearance of the sargassum fish, and the imitative colouring of the lizard fish. ■ Other remarkable adaptations include the poisonous tentacles of the Portuguese man-of-war; the poisonous spike in the tail of the bottom-feeding stingray; the barbed needles of the spiny urchin; and the "self-made" camouflage of certain crabs, who grow sea anemones and sponges on their backs. For every mechanism of attack there is a counter-mechanism of defence.

1

3

4

2

1. *Spiny Lobster Sheds its Shell*
2. *Porcupine Fish Erects Sharp Spines*
3. *Sargassum Fish Looks Like Weed it Lives in*
4. *Lizard Fish*
5. *Green Turtle Wears Heavy Suit of Armour*

FAR LEFT: *A Parrotfish Hides Beneath Antlers of Staghorn Coral*

5

The newest potential reef-dweller is man. With self-contained underwater breathing apparatus (SCUBA) or simply with mask and flippers, human beings can now explore freely the wonders of this submarine world, can observe and photograph its scenic beauty, its colourful living creatures. In specially constructed shelters, man may spend days, weeks, or longer living in the reef—studying its mysteries—harvesting its plenty. Enthusiasts have even predicted that surgeons may some day equip human beings with "gills", like fishes, for staying underwater indefinitely. ■ By that time, one hopes, the world's coral reefs will still exist unspoiled, their balance of life undisturbed by indiscriminate human killers, or "civilized" pollution. Already, once-common species are beginning to grow rare, and many reef creatures have learned to fear the most powerful of predators, man. ■ But if properly used, the beauty of the reef and its busy and fascinating life will be around forever—for man's pleasure, admiration, and profit.

Air Tank, Mask and Flippers Allow Leisurely Exploration of Reef

*Reef-Dwelling Tubeworm
Raises its Flowerlike Head*

Coral reefs take three principal forms. In *fringing reefs*, the reefs grow on or near the shores of stable land masses. In *barrier reefs*, broad, shallow lagoons separate the land from the reef. Barrier reefs are most often formed near sinking land masses, or may be descendants of fringing reefs, since reefs grow out from shore, leaving a lagoon behind when attached to stable shores. *Atolls* are products of the sinking of islands, mostly volcanic and in the Pacific. Atoll formation had puzzled geologists until Darwin's theory of submergence. All types of reefs, since they grow near the water's surface, may lead to island formation.

Fringing Reef

Barrier Reef

Efforts to preserve the wonder and beauty of the undersea world for the enjoyment of all have resulted in the creation of the John Pennekamp Coral Reef State Park, off Key Largo, Florida, America. This 75-square-mile coral wonderland, only 25 miles from bustling Miami Beach, is the world's first totally underwater park. Many of the pictures in this book were made here. Three miles from Key Largo's shore, this undersea preserve is the northernmost of a chain of reefs that extends some 220 miles south and west into the Gulf of Mexico

Atoll

JOHN PENNEKAMP CORAL REEF STATE PARK ALSO DESIGNATED AS KEY LARGO CORAL REEF PRESERVE

NOTE: *Coral reefs occur in the subtropical and tropical seas of the world, between latitudes 28°N and 28°S. The coral-reef life described in this book is that characteristic of reefs off the Florida coast, the Bahamas and the nearby West Indies. Names given for fishes and other animals are those in common use in this area*

INDEX

BACK ENDPAPERS